The journey to publish this book has been essential in my healing process. On April 28, 2021, I was diagnosed with triple-negative breast cancer. With one phone call the trajectory of my life was forever changed. The unwavering support of my family and friends throughout this process will never be forgotten. This book is dedicated to my dream team: my husband, parents, sister, BFF, and cousin. Each of these people took me to doctor's appointments, chemotherapy infusions, ER trips, or prayed with me every week. Words could never express how truly grateful I am to have the inner circle that I do. The raw emotions that accompanied the roller coaster that is my breast cancer story are found within the pages of this book. Additionally, there is space for you to reflect on your own feelings as you read through each of my poems.

The Uninvited Guest

Contents

The Uninvited Guest

It was finally here...my big event that I worked
so hard to plan

Months of time and preparation went into this
to ensure I knew just how things would be ran

The decorations and theme were out of this
world with the color scheme perfected to
a "T"

My hair, my make-up, and outfit were planned
to be the best version of me

The menu was thoroughly laid out to ensure
that all my guests' diets were accommodated

Saying that people should enjoy themselves is
simply understated

As the time approached and my guests arrived
the excitement started to heighten

The vibe was great, the music was playing, and
smiles around the room continued to brighten

Then suddenly, an uninvited guest barged their
way through my door

No knock, no doorbell, not even a hello...all
politeness she just ignored

She stormed in the party leaving things in
disarray as if her invite got lost in the mail

Her plan was to come and enjoy herself
operating like a ship without a sail

I began to watch all my hard work start to
quickly dwindle away

My guests were disturbed, the vibe was ruined,
it was confirmed she couldn't stay

I never invited her to the party, so I owed her
no niceties

She was in my house, invading my space,
creating havoc all around me

I quickly approached her, stared her in the eyes,
and at first didn't say a word

I wanted her to feel my presence my voice
didn't need to be heard

I needed her to see that even though some
damage had definitely been done

I was stopping her in her tracks, so she should
turn and run

She might have thought this was fun and
games, but my work here is not done

cancer as my uninvited guest your stay is
undoubtedly overdue

The word guest means this is not your home, so
LEAVE I didn't invite you!

The title The Uninvited Guest dropped in my spirit very early on in my cancer journey. While I didn't invite cancer into my life, I was confident that it wouldn't stay, so I refer to it as a guest. The title inspired me to write this poem and ultimately keep writing to create this book.

I have always enjoyed writing, but writing took on a different purpose after I was diagnosed with breast cancer. Writing quickly became my life raft when I was sinking in a sea of pain, uncertainty, and defeat. What do you do to help you get through challenging times in your life? Have you ever used journaling to release your emotions? I encourage you to reflect on each of the poems that I share in this book. Look at the questions I ask and express your feelings in the space provided.

_____

_____

_____

_____

_____

_____

_____

The Call

Who would've thought that one little call
could change my life's trajectory

A call from the doctor saying those words
I'm sorry, but you are not cancer free

Before this day I had plans that were finally
falling in place

I was living an abundant life filled with ups
and downs, but mostly God's grace

Now for a short moment I felt as though
grace was no longer surrounding me

It was as if my place securely in His arms
could no longer be

Although that's how I felt for a quick
moment on a very, very low day

I realize that my God is faithful and would
never turn away

So instead of asking why me or saying God
don't let this be

I'm standing here ready for battle, because
I won't just let cancer take me

My life did change with one phone call,
and it will never be the same

Even with all these new uncertainties there's
no doubt that my God does reign

I prayed for the ability to help others so many times before

I just had no idea that this was what my God would have in store

So, although this battle won't be easy, I'm choosing to believe

That call was the jumpstart to my new beginning and all that I must achieve

I am not fighting just for me, but for all of you too

My sisters don't delay get yourself checked out it's something you have to do

Tomorrow isn't promised so every day we must live to the fullest degree

cancer may have entered in my world, but I'm not letting it have me!

On April 28, 2021, I received a call that forever changed my life. Hearing the words "I'm sorry, but you have breast cancer." were words that I never imagined being spoken to me. Yet, once they were my life was forever changed. Has there been a conversation in your life that changed everything for you? Has something you experienced caused a drastic change in your life? What was that situation? How did your life change whether it was positive or negative?

_____

_____

_____

_____

_____

_____

_____

_____

_____

You're Really Bald

Yes, I do have mirrors throughout my house
that remind me every day

I am truly and absolutely bald there's no
getting around that in any kind of way

In case you're wondering I'm not bald by
choice…in fact it was never my plan

Yet, God seemed to think I could handle it so
with this bald idea He ran

He told me you're strong ignore the stares
that will often come your way

I try to embrace it, hold my head up high
regardless of what people tend to say

Yet somedays it's just too hot to cover my
head so my bald head has to do

Chemo put me in early menopause, so hot
flashes make their way through

I won't lie sometimes it becomes a game and I
intentionally walk bald and free

Let everyone else be the uncomfortable ones
while I walk around just being me

Please know I'm so much more than my hair
which cancer stole from me

Yet sometimes those who are the closest
forget how harmful words can be

These days I rarely feel beautiful it's normally
the opposite you see

But I still put on the brave face for all the
world and exude a life filled with glee

Nobody wants to hear that you're hurting
inside and begging God for grace

They want to tell you how strong you are and
to keep that smile on your face

If I can leave you with a little advice that you
may remember even after today

Be kind to people, think before you speak and
know us bald women are beautiful in
every way!

After being diagnosed with breast cancer I received a lot of unique questions and comments. I realized that people may say certain things, with no malintent but still cause pain. I wrote this poem after someone in my circle told me I was "Really Bald". They were right...I was really bald, but that didn't take away the sting I felt from the piercing words. The tongue is a powerful thing. Have you ever said something to someone that you wish you could take back? Or has someone said something to you and unintentionally caused you pain? How did you get past that situation? What can you do to ensure that you choose to use your speech to uplift people?

_____

_____

_____

_____

_____

_____

_____

It's Enough

The fake smile you put on to give off the perception that everything is okay

Yes, it's enough

The unsettling feeling that resides in the pit of your stomach that just won't seem to go away

I am confident that it's enough

The unwavering guilt you feel about the decisions of your past

I know it's enough

The tears that get stuck in your throat as you swallow to keep on the brave face

You can release them...It is surely enough

The weight that rests on your shoulders and prevents you from holding your head up high

I promise you...it's enough

The strength that you can't muster up to say goodbye

You have to believe...it's enough

He's waiting patiently for you to believe that It's enough

He died on the cross so that you could see it's enough

Stop beating yourself up and feeling defeated...you're not alone

We are all going into, fighting through, or coming out of that very place

So, at what point are you willing to see God's grace and know...It's enough!

This poem was written for my best friend after she called me emotionally distraught. When I stopped to pray for her God gave me these words, and I had to put it on paper. As I've traveled through my breast cancer journey, I have had to remind myself that God's grace is sufficient to get me through even my lowest moments. How do you encourage those you care about when they're facing a difficult time in their life? Has there ever been a time when you had to remind yourself that God's grace is enough? What did you do during that situation? How have you helped others who are battling feelings of despair?

_____

_____

_____

_____

_____

_____

_____

_____

It's You

As I try to quiet the consistent storm that my
stomach encounters

It's You

When the fatigue is so overwhelming that
parting my lips to eat seems like a chore

It's You

As I try to juggle the day-to-day appointments,
blood work, and scans I start to lose myself
then

It's You

When the phone rings with another call giving
unfavorable test results

It's You

As tears stream down my face only to land in
the pile of hair that was forced to leave my
scalp

It's You

As I try to be strong for everyone else leaving
nothing left for myself

It's You

When giving up seems so much easier there's
a light that shines through the darkness and

It's You

You are the one who scoops me up no matter
how many times I fall

You are the one that picks up the phone and
knows the exact right time to call

You are the one who says exactly what I need
to hear, it was as if you read my mind

You are the one who ushers in peace even
when there was none I could find

You are the one who allowed your shirt to be
soaked with my tears

You are the one who found a way to calm my
worst fears

It's You

My husband, my kids, my parents, and sister
too, my family, my BFF, my Sorors, and my
friends

It's All of You!!!

I have been blessed with an amazing group of family and friends who have been there to support me through my cancer journey. It's You is dedicated to all of them for the love they have shown me during this difficult time. I recognize that not everyone has someone to support them through trying situations. Is there someone in your life that you're thankful for? If so, reflect on the things they have done that have impacted your life. Have you found yourself supporting someone else? Would you prefer to go through a difficult time with or without support? Do you consider yourself to be an introvert or an extravert? Do you think your personality plays a role in how you approach challenges within your life?

_____

_____

_____

_____

_____

_____

_____

I Can Smell the Sunshine

Today was different from those before in
fact my senses feel renewed

The sun seems brighter, flowers smell
sweeter, and birds are more melodious too

Since I began this journey, my life has been
a nonstop roller coaster

I tried to get off 1,000 times, but I keep
going upside down over and over

Although I still can't get off the ride it finally
slowed down for me

Long enough to smell the sunshine and
remember how calming peace can be

I feel hopeful, encouraged, and positive
even if only for today

With all the difficult news I have been
getting my God still made a way

He remined me that He is in control even
when hope seems so dim

If I continue to focus on His love, I know I'll
always win

So, when these days that are vivacious with
light just happen to come my way

I'll enjoy every moment of them because I
know they cannot stay

Today I'll lay and bask in the sun as the
beams adorn my face

It's as if God Himself is sending his love and
his arms to create a warm embrace

The rays of the sun radiate my body and
make my life feel renewed

It's amazing how one little positive thing
can set everything to a different tune

Regardless, of the past I choose to be
thankful for this remarkably great day

Today I vividly smell the sunshine and that
joy can't be taken away!

My husband and I celebrated our 5-year wedding anniversary in the midst of my 16 rounds of chemotherapy. Although we couldn't celebrate like we wanted to we did a quick trip to a local beach. Even though it wasn't traditional beach weather I enjoyed every minute of it. It gave me the opportunity to feel like a normal person. The combination of the waves crashing, the feeling of the sand between my toes, the smell of the flowers blooming, and the warmth from the sun glaring was therapeutic. It was as if I could actually smell the sunshine. Can you recall a place you visited that brought you peace and tranquility? What do you remember most about that place? What trying circumstance were you experiencing in your life? Are there any places you would like to go in the future that will bring you happiness?

_____

_____

_____

_____

_____

_____

_____

How Are You?

The number of times I'm asked that question a day
has now sored to new heights

The end of April threw me a curve ball that was
nowhere in my sights

Often times I'm asked that question because it's
part of a greeting to me

The expectation is that it's never actually met with
any authenticity

See the reply they're most likely looking for is I'm
doing great and you?

Which I could gladly say with a smile, but that
would be so untrue

My honest reply would most likely ruin their sunny
pleasant day

Make them regret even asking the question and
next time just look the opposite way

Other times I'm asked it because the individual
really does care about me

But that's when I'm the most torn, do I tell them
the truth or stick with a pleasantry

That question carries so much more weight than
people really know

To be honest I even had no idea how deep the
emotions from it could grow

If you're in a position like me where you are
fighting an uninvited guest

One second you feel like you're going to break, but
the next you're passing the test

Some days you may have to pull over the car,
because your emotions have taken over

Do I scream, do I cry, do I run, or just stand still
and wait for my four-leaf clover

The reality is I don't believe in luck so no need to
even pretend

God allowed this uninvited guest to breach my
doorway so only He can make the pain end

So instead of questioning why me or complaining
I'm trying to focus on positivity

I may look around just to stay rooted, but in my
heart, you will find no envy

Although this ship of my life seems to be traveling
through the storm with no shore in sight

Peace comes from knowing God is my captain in
the darkness He's ALWAYS light

So little c, yes that's how I refer to cancer, your
time is limited with me

If a fight is what you want, then a fight is what
you'll get, I'm claiming victory!

The question "How Are You?" has become a common greeting, but most people rarely expect an earnest answer. After being diagnosed this greeting takes on a whole new meaning. Is there a phrase that you've heard throughout your life that previously had no meaning, but an event occurred and changed your perspective? Think of a phrase that you often say, or a question that you ask that could deeply impact someone? Are you asking a question to others that could cause them some unintended pain? Is there something that is frequently said to you that you find frustrating? If so, have you communicated your frustrations to others?

_____

_____

_____

_____

_____

_____

_____

_____

After the Bell

Everyone thinks I should be so happy,
feeling accomplished and so free

Don't get me wrong I am thankful for
how far God has brought me

Yet that feeling of happiness and joy
that I long for is nowhere to be found

I'm fighting off feelings of despair,
uncertainty, and anxiety that are
all around

There are clouds filling my sky that
refuse to let the sun break through

I know the sun is there I can feel its
warmth, but this feeling just won't do

No matter which way I turn and
regardless of how fast I run

These clouds keep blocking my
sunshine from a battle that I
have overcome

I'm not sure what I'm supposed to do or
exactly how I should feel

I'm determined to keep fighting, but on
the inside this pain is all too real

As crazy as it sounds there was some
normality to my chemo days

I had a plan, a routine, a team and I
was no longer running in a maze

Although the side effects were the worst
part the normalcy gave me peace

Now that it's gone chaos has returned
and I don't know when I'll get a release

Reality is with each day that passes the
next battle is quickly approaching

There's no time to waste I'm fighting
cancer who on my body is
rapidly encroaching

The bell was rung, and 16 rounds of
chemo was all left behind

Today I'm searching for the warrior
inside, my light is determined to shine!

After enduring 16 rounds of chemotherapy my family and friends decided to celebrate with me on the day of my last infusion. Due to the pandemic, we had a virtual celebration to celebrate this milestone in my treatment. My family and friends posted pictures of them in their Team Pam shirts all over social media. I was truly overwhelmed by the love and support they showed me. Yet, there was still a part of me that felt sadness when my chemotherapy was completed. Have you ever experienced a painful situation, but you were sad when the experience came to an end? Why do you think a person could find pain and comfort in a situation? Do all situations have to be positive or negative, or can a situation cause an individual to experience multiple emotions?

_____

_____

_____

_____

_____

_____

_____

Fighting Through the Pain

I am writing this through the tears that
continue to run down my face

I try to chase them with my hand, but they just
continue to escape

I tell myself to smile and act happy like
everything is okay

Yet when I am alone with my thoughts, there
is no sight of a brand-new day

cancer has taken so many parts of me, but I
thought I was handling it well

Somehow, I ended up in this cage of
brokenness feeling like I'm knocking on the
gates of hell

I'm trying to fight as hard as I can searching for
the warrior in me

Yet I feel like I'm losing this battle, I need
answers on how to break free

I'm overwhelmed by the insecurities that
come with being this new me

I don't have the luxury of feeling confident
and vibrant like others can be

Only those who have gone through this
journey will ever really know

What it is like to look in a mirror and the pain
constantly seems to grow

I silently pray Lord please restore me to some
form of what I used to love

I hate what I see...there I said it, and I know
that feeling isn't from above

Yet these emotions are all too real and I'm
embracing all of me

The good, the bad, the beautiful, the ugly, I
can no longer mask what you see

Maybe tomorrow will be better and these
feelings will drift away

But as for today all I can express is my raw
pain which I beg not to stay.

As I looked in the mirror every day, I watched the woman I once knew slowly fade away. I began not to recognize myself and at times even hated the version of myself that stared back at me. Have you ever looked in the mirror and experienced feelings of sadness, frustration, or anger? Take a moment to reflect on that time in your life. What was causing the frustration? What did you do to overcome those feelings? If you are currently feeling this way, what do you need to overcome these emotions? What steps do you need to take to return to a place where you love yourself?

_____

_____

_____

_____

_____

_____

_____

_____

Dear Girls

Dear Girls,

It has taken me a long time to get up the strength to write this letter to you. Before the diagnosis I took for granted all that you have allowed me to do. I never realized that you all were such a huge part of my identity. Since the age of 8 when you entered my life, I had no idea what you'd truly mean to me. As we grew together you became a part of the woman others would see. You gave me curves in all the right places making my clothes fit perfectly. As I looked at you every day in the mirror, I took you for granted and often complained. Yet, you still allowed me to nurse my sons an experience so beautiful I cannot explain. For that I am forever grateful and acknowledge the role that you both played. Even as today while I embrace my womanhood through all the joy and pain you both stayed. A fibroid removal, 2 c-sections, and now a breast cancer diagnosis has plagued me. When they told me they wanted to amputate you all I prayed this was not my reality. I grieved for you both as if you were already gone and tried to come up with a way to extend your life. There must be some way to alleviate this disease without enduring all this pain and strife. At the end of the day, I came to a conclusion that was harder than you will ever know. Girls I love you; I appreciate everything you have done for me, but you are trying to kill me...so you have to go!

I wrote this letter to my breast after a session I had with my therapist. I was having a very difficult time accepting the need for a bilateral mastectomy. I felt like cancer had already stolen so much from me, but ultimately the realization that they were trying to take my life changed everything. Think about the most challenging decision you have made in your life. Why was the decision so difficult? What ultimately made you come to your final decision? How do you feel now that you have made that decision?

_____

_____

_____

_____

_____

_____

_____

_____

_____

Pages of Reflection

_____

_____

_____

_____

_____

_____

_____

_____

_____

_____

_____

_____

_____

_____

_____

Made in the USA
Middletown, DE
22 April 2022

64644255R00042